How Tall Is God?

Written and
Illustrated by

Phillip W.
Rodgers

BEES
with Flashlights

Bees With Flashlights, LLC
www.beeswithflashlights.com

Discovering God Series

For more information and fun, please visit
www.DiscoveringGodSeries.com

How Tall Is God? © 2003 by Phillip W. Rodgers
Published by Bees With Flashlights, LLC.
All rights reserved.

A special thanks to Kay Arthur, Tim LaHaye, Jan Silvious, Vicky Overcash,
Susan Iles, Jeannie St. John Taylor, Bill and Barbara Rodgers,
Robert and Barbara Dempsey, and Dan Penwell for all their help and support.

ISBN: 978-0-9844176-0-5

Printed in the
United States of America.
072012-1r-2000-JO-37040

To
Stephanie,
Kaylee, and
Abby...

and children
everywhere who are
discovering God

Thunder and lightning streaks shook the dark night, and Bailey the bear cub was shaking with fright.

His father had tucked him snug into bed
when Bailey sat up and quietly said,

"How tall is God, Dad? I bet that you know.
Is He taller than mountains covered with snow?"

"Can He see over skyscapers, flagpoles, and trees?
Could the tallest giraffe reach up to God's knees?"

"That's a very good question, something quite rare.
But why do you ask, my thoughtful young bear?"

"Well, sometimes there's shadows
up on my ceiling
that give me the spookiest,
scariest feeling.

Is God tall enough
to watch over me,
keeping me safe when
it's too dark to see?"

Dad remembered a time when he had been small
and didn't yet know that God was so tall.

"God's **very big**, son," Dad said with a nod.
"There's no building or mountain as big as our God."

"As high as the sky, the moon, and the stars,
past earth and the sun, to Pluto and Mars,
as far and as wide as the deepest of space,
God's there, and He touches each faraway place!"

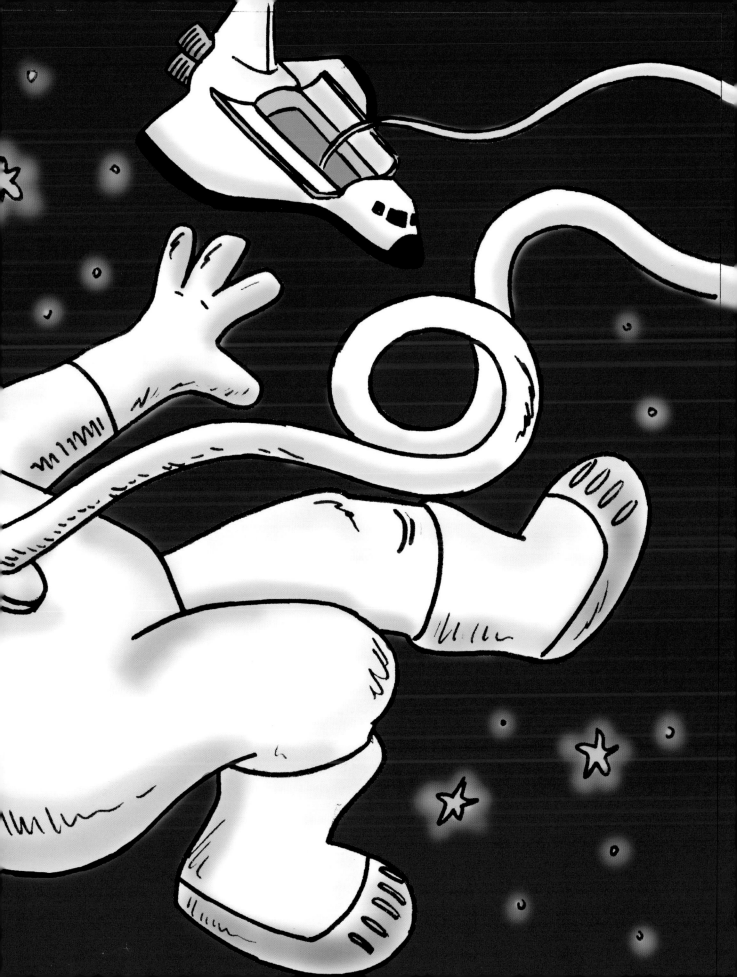

"God puts the green leaves on the tallest of trees
and guides the white clouds over mountains and seas.

These are only a few of the things God can do,
so I'm sure He'll watch out for a young cub like you."

"He may have looked big,
but to God he was small;

David flung one smooth stone,
and then God made him fall."

"High up in the sky He placed a bright star
for shepherds and wise men to see from afar.

His angels came down from heaven to earth
and sang 'Peace, goodwill!' at Jesus's birth."

"God's love is enormous! He's near to us all
so He's ready to help us the moment we call.

Now you can be sure when you run out to play
that God will be with you throughout the whole day."

"Wow! God really *is* tall!" Bailey said with a smile.
"His love reaches longer than even a mile!"

"He's bigger than any tall building I see,
but He isn't too big to care about me."

"I'm sure God can see me, and even much more,
from my walls to the ceiling and down to the floor.

Because God is with me, I'm no longer afraid.
My fear of the dark is beginning to fade!"

So Dad gave Bailey a kiss and a hug
and said, "Sweet dreams, my little bear cub."

"God will watch over you
all through the night."

Bailey pulled up his blanket.
Dad turned out the light.

It's the single most important question your child will ever ask.

At some point in everyone's life, the question, "Who is God?" will demand an answer. This question shapes every facet of a person's life. Without a working knowledge of our Creator and His character, children are left with a worldview driven by transient personal feelings and motives. Because of the self-centered nature of this worldview, apathy is often its offspring. In contrast, a God-centered worldview focused on God's perspective of right and wrong can help a child find a deeper purpose and meaning for their life by understanding God's love for others and how that relates to them. Studies have shown that the best time to teach this important lesson is between the preschool and early elementary years. Because basic values are determined during these years, known as the "formative years," they should be considered possibly the most important in a person's life.

Designed to encourage a God-centered worldview, the "Discovering God Series" tackles those hard-to-answer questions children ask about God through endearing stories that intrigue them to learn more. Based on biblical truths, each book focuses on a different characteristic of our Creator and is written in terms that children understand. Children love the poetry and bright illustrations as well as the fun, whimsical and thought-provoking stories following the adventures of a young bear named Bailey.

About the Author

As a child, **Phillip W. Rodgers** occupied a large portion of his time drawing and writing. He was inspired by Walt Disney and Charles Shulz. Just like his childhood heros, Phillip entertains people through his artwork, stories and characters.

Phillip resides in Ringgold, GA with his wife Stephanie, and their two girls, Kaylee and Abby. He is a sought-after speaker and teacher, traveling to various venues inspiring children and adults to "discover God."